To the many women in my life who inspire me every day:

The Guevarra Girls, especially my Grandma Dorothy,
who taught me everything I know about life and love.
The Whibbs Women, who taught me that humor can help you
get through even the darkest of days. Keep fighting, Betsy!
The Theriault Tribe that has made me a part of the family.

And a special thanks to Impact 10__ __ __ __ __der
Community Institute (especially Shannon). Thank you for
helping make this book a reality!

"The more that you read, the more things you will know. The
more that you learn, the more places you'll go."

—Dr. Seuss

www.mascotbooks.com

P is for Pelican: The ABCs of Pensacola

Third Printing

For more information, please contact:
Mascot Books
620 Herndon Parkway #320
Herndon, VA 20170
info@mascotbooks.com

Library of Congress Control Number: 2016920959

CPSIA Code: PRT0418C
ISBN-13: 978-1-68401-115-5

Printed in the United States

P is for Pelican
The ABCs of
PENSACOLA

Anna Whibbs Theriault

Illustrated by Chiara Civati

A a
is for Argos playing strong in the fall.

Bb is for Blue Angels flying past the Beach Ball.

Cc is for Castles built with seashells and sand.

Dd is for Dolphins we can see from the land.

Ee is for Egret with feathers of white.

Ff is for Forts that stand dark in the night.

Gg is for Gulf Waters washing up on the shore.

Hh is for Historic Village
always teaching us more.

Ii is for Ice Cream that cools us off when the heat is too much.

Jj is for Jellyfish. Look, but don't touch!

 **is for Kite dancing high in the air.**

Ll is for Lighthouse sitting atop winding stairs.

is for Maritime Park where we gather as one.

MUSEUM
NAVAL AVIATION

 is for Naval Museum where we learn and have fun.

**is for Orchestra
filling the air
with music so
sweet.**

is for Pelican in the air...

And on the street...

 **is for Quietwater Beach where new friends say hello.**

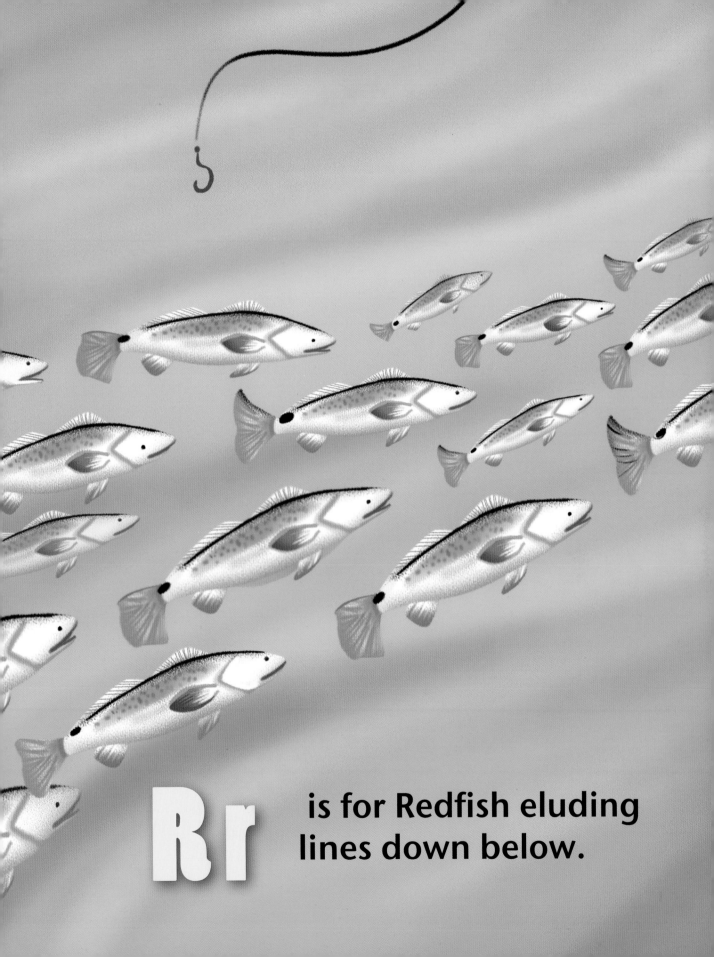

Rr is for Redfish eluding
lines down below.

Ss is for Surfer catching spray in one hand.

Tt is for Turtles making their way through the sand.

U u

is for Umbrellas decorating the shore with cheer.

CHAPPIE

GENERAL DANIEL JAMES, JR
FEB. 11, 1920 – FEB. 25, 1978

AMERICA'S FIRST AFRICAN
AMERICAN FOUR STAR GENERAL
U.S.A.F.

Vv is for Veterans
we honor
each year.

 is for Wahoos Stadium that lights up the dark.

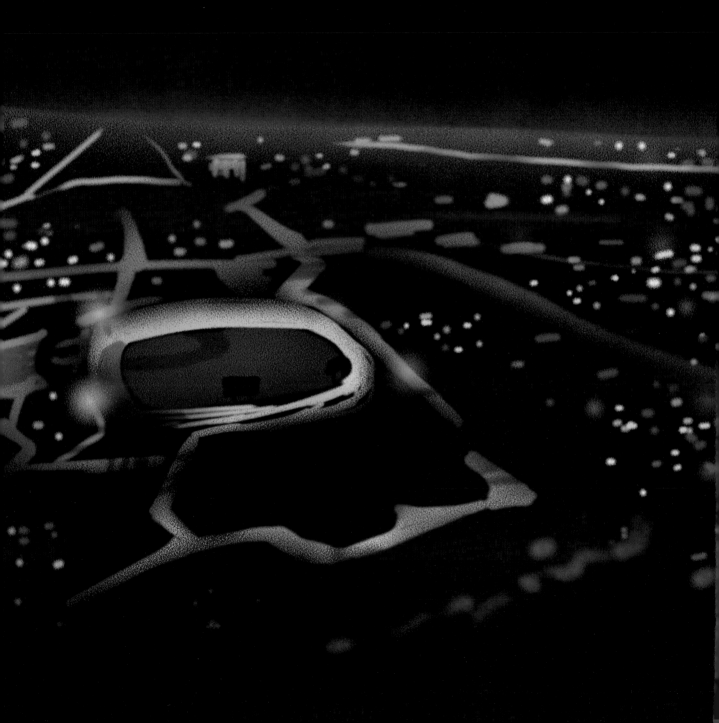

 is for Xylophone
we play at the park.

 **is for the new downtown YMCA.**

Zz is for Zoom as cars fly around Five Flags Speedway.

Thank you for reading about our lovely town.
How many Pensacola ABCs can you find by driving
around?

Argos (UWF)
Blue Angels/Beach Ball
Castles
Dolphins
Egret
Forts
Gulf Islands National Seashore
Historic Pensacola Village
Ice Cream (Bubba's Sweet Shop)
Jellyfish
Kites
Lighthouse
Maritime Park
Naval Museum
Orchestra
Pelicans
Quietwater Beach
Redfish
Surfer
Turtles
Umbrellas
Veterans Memorial Park
Wahoos Stadium
Xylophone
YMCA
Zoom (Five Flags Speedway)

Thank you to all of the men and women of the Armed Forces who fight every day to protect our freedom. A special thanks to the members of my family who serve now or have in the past, Vince Whibbs, Benjamin Guevarra, James Bentley, Mark Whibbs, Michael Vogel Sr., Michael Vogel Jr., Carlos Guevarra, Sharon Burnham, Robin Fike, Matt Frasse, Christopher Frasse, Jack Brown, John Ray, Hunter Vickrey, James Ralls, and Tristan Rizzi. The sacrifices that you have made for our country will not be forgotten!

About the Author

Anna Whibbs Theriault lives in Pensacola with her husband, two boys, and a large (boisterous) extended family. Anna was born and raised in Pensacola and grew up watching the area blossom into the coastal community that it is today. The family enjoys the many beach activities available along the Emerald Coast, including surfing, paddle-boarding, fishing, and boating. Anna considers herself blessed to call this little piece of paradise home. Anna is also the author of *Goodnight Pensacola.*